KEEPING Q
A Guide to Dome
Commercial Man

Katie Thear

Broad Leys Publishing Company, Essex.

Keeping Quail: A Guide to Domestic and
Commercial Management

First edition: 1987

Second edition: 1994

Copyright © 1987 and 1994. Katie Thear

Printed and bound by J.B. Offset Printers (Marks Tey) Ltd
Published by Broad Leys Publishing Company, Buriton House,
Station Road, Newport, Saffron Walden, Essex CB11 3PL.

A catalogue record for this book is available from the British Library

ISBN 0 906137 22 5

Details of publications produced by Broad Leys Publishing Company
are available from:
Broad Leys Publishing Company, Buriton House, Station Road,
Newport, Saffron Walden, Essex CB11 3PL, United Kingdom.
Telephone: (0799) 540 922 Fax: (0799) 541 367

Contents

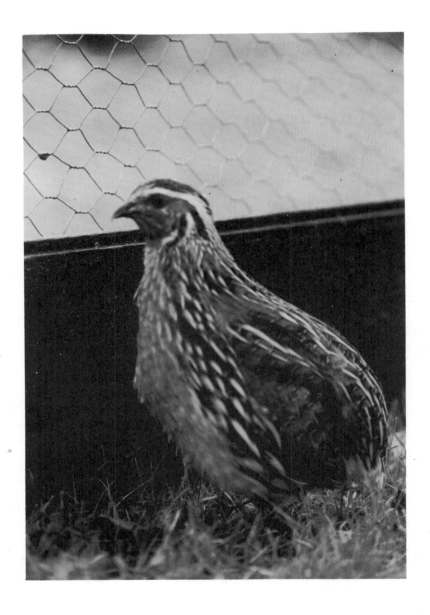

Coturnix laying quail. The male in an outside breeding pen

Introduction

Quail are classified as game birds, sharing the same family as pheasants and partridges. Although there are over forty different species of quail in the world, the number of species kept domestically or commercially, or as ornamental aviary birds, is quite small. The book concentrates, therefore, on the breeding and management of those species, notably the Coturnix laying strains, the Bobwhite meat breeds, and the ornamental aviary breeds such as the Chinese Painted quail. However, the book does not neglect the wider scale in relation to overall breed development and diversification.

The first edition of this book was published in 1987. It has sold all over the world and, as a result, I have received letters from many different countries. I am grateful to all those who sent in suggestions and contributions, and am pleased to be able to include them in this new edition. I hope that readers will continue to contact me about any inclusions for the next edition.

Since the last edition there has been new legislation concerning the preparation and sale of meat products in Britain and the EC. The chapter on Table Quail reflects these changes, providing advice for all those who may be considering the marketing of quail products. The Reference section has also been brought up to date so that anyone looking for sources of stock and equipment will be able to find the appropriate contacts.

I hope that quail breeders, producers, hobbyists, schools and agricultural colleges, and indeed anyone interested in these fascinating little birds will find something of interest within these pages.

Katie Thear, Newport, 1994

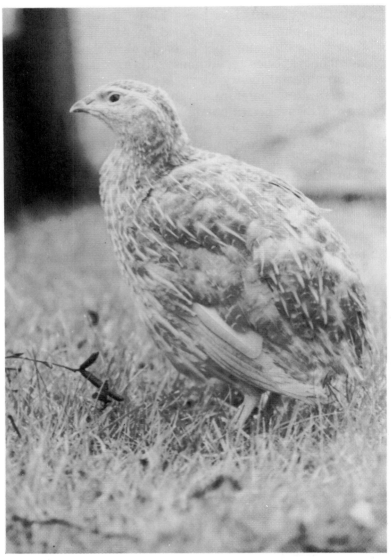

Female of the Fawn Coturnix laying quail. (See also the outside front cover!)

History

The earliest known representation of the quail is in Egyptian hieroglyphics, when the little bird was presumably common enough and important enough to merit a place in the alphabet. It is not known what the breed development has been over the centuries, but there are two closely related species in the wild, the Common or European quail, *Coturnix coturnix*, and the Eurasian or Pharoah quail, *Coturnix communis*. The chances are that these were both derived from a common source in the past. In the Americas, there is a quite different strain in the Bobwhite quail, *Colinus species*, and worldwide, there are thirteen other sub-groupings of quail.

Remains of the Coturnix quail have been found in Upper Pleistocene rocks in Britain, notably in Chudleigh Cave and Kent's Cave in Devon, Hoe Grange Cave in Derbyshire and Kirkdale Cave in Yorkshire.

In the Bible, there is reference to how food was brought to the starving Israelites in the wilderness:

'There went forth a wind from the Lord and brought quails from the sea.'

They were kept as aviary birds by the early Greeks whose interests seem to have extended to their fighting as well as their culinary qualities. Dionysius and Aristotle refer to them, as well as the Roman writer Pliny.

Quails are mentioned in eighth century Saxon writings, and later by the seventeenth century poet John Clare in his bird listings for East Anglia.

Shakespeare refers to the ancient practice of quail fighting in *Antony and Cleopatra*, when Antony bemoans the fact that Caesar's chances of winning are greater than his:

'His cocks do win the battle still of mine when it is all to naught, and his quails ever beat mine, inhooped, at odds.'

Beethoven utilizes the call of the quail (*wet my lips*) in his music. See if you can spot it in his *Pastoral Symphony*!
Gilbert White, the eighteenth century vicar of Selborne, and author of that great classic of natural history, *The Natural History of Selborne*, makes several references to hearing *'quail calls'* in the summer months.

In 1859, Mrs. Beeton had this to say:

Early representations of the quail

Painted relief from the
tomb of Seti 1 at Thebes

Section of the Hunefer
papyrus scroll

Reliefs from the Temple of
Seti 1 at Abydos

Woodcut from *Mrs Beeton's
Book of Household
Management*, 1861.

Woodcut from Thomas
Bewick's *History of Birds*,
1820

'Quails are almost universally diffused over Europe, Asia and Africa, in the autumn, and returning again in the spring, frequently alighting in their passage on many of the islands of the Archipelago, which, with their vast numbers, they almost completely cover ... It appears highly probable that the quails which supplied the Israelites with food during their journey through the wilderness, were sent by a wind from the south-west, sweeping over Eqypt towards the shores of the Red Sea. In England they are not very numerous, although they breed in it; and many of them are said to remain throughout the year, changing their quarters from the interior parts of the country for the seacoast.'

Sir Herbert Maxwell reported that:

'There was a moderate immigration in 1893', and commented that, *'the fecundity of the species must be prodigious; millions being taken in nets during their spring and autumn migrations across the Mediterranean'*. These went, he claimed, *'to the great cities of Europe, where hundreds of thousands are consumed at the tables of wealthy persons'*.

The quail's retiring habit has given rise to the verb: to quail. The Reverend Patrick Bronte makes use of it in a letter to Ellen Hussey in 1885, when he refers to Mrs Gaskell's undertaking to write the life of his daughter Charlotte:

'No quailing, Mrs Gaskell! No drawing back!'

The quail is the state bird of California and is a relatively common sight. I saw several of the attractive little California quail, *Lophortyx californica*, on the edge of lake Cachuma.

In recent years, a considerable quail industry has grown in the United States, Japan, Italy, France and Britain. This is to cater for the gourmet interest in quails' eggs and delicatessen table birds. In Japan, the quail also has the dubious distinction of being bred for laboratory testing.

But perhaps the last word should go to a schoolboy, Alex Smith, who sent me the following poem about the quail, and which I was pleased to include in the first edition. I don't think that any of the writers of ancient civilizations have bettered his description:

'Short and plump,
Timid but inquisitive;
Dull but pretty,
Not very clever,
But a long way from silly.'

About the quail

There is a wide variety of breeds, adapted to varying climates and conditions throughout the world, but in this brief look at the general characteristics of quail, I have concentrated on the more common breeds.

Most quails are birds of the undergrowth which, depending on the area, may be tall grasses, dense bush, shrub thickets, overgrown fields, meadows, plantations or savannahs. They are essentially shy retiring birds which will 'quail' with fear into the shadow and security of the undergrowth. When really disturbed however, they will break cover like pheasants, and fly straight up into the air with a characteristic whirring of wings.

Ground orientation

Most are ground-orientated in that they spend most of their time on the ground in the wild, except when they are migrating or disturbed in some way. Some are more ground-orientated than others. The Chinese Painted quail, for example, is like a small mouse scuttling about on the ground, resorting to occasional short flights where necessary. The Bobwhite, by comparison, likes to fly and perch. It is important, therefore, to make adequate provision for such behaviour within an aviary system. Clumps of grass or shrubs are needed to provide cover, with a couple of branches for perching.

Toes and claws

Most breeds of quail have long toes and claws, an adaptation for scratching for insectivorous foods. In an aviary there is usually provision for this, but if there is only a concrete run, do make sure they have an area where fine soil, sand or wood shavings can be made available. In a battery cage system, this is not possible, and it is one of the reasons why I dislike the battery system for any bird or poultry, because it does not provide conditions for them to exercise their natural instincts.

If the quails do not have scratching conditions where their claws are kept worn down, it may be necessary to trim them. To do this, hold the bird gently in one hand, using the fingers

Characteristics of the quail

Long sharp beak ideal for picking up grains and insects

Sharp eyesight provides protection against predators such as hawks in the wild

Strong claws scratch the soil to reveal insectivorous food

Stippled feather markings provide camouflage in the long grass or undergrowth

to keep the limb steady, then clip the claws with nail clippers. Do this in a good light so that you can see where the blood vessel within the claw ends, so that the cut is made beyond it. Ordinary nail clippers of the kind sold in chemist shops are ideal for this task.

The beak

The quail's beak is long, pointed and sharp, ideally suited for pecking small insects, grains or for shredding small pieces of vegetation. It can also be an aggressive weapon if one quail decides to attack another. In some intensive units, quails are debeaked; the upper beak is trimmed back so that it is shorter than the lower one, but I find such a practice repugnant. It is only a short-term solution anyway, for it usually grows back. Another practice, more common in the USA than in Britain, is to use beak rings. These are open rings which have the ends inserted into the nostrils and then pinched together with pliers. Again, I would not advise such an inhumane approach.

In the wild, the beak is kept relatively short by access to a range of natural materials. In captivity it is a good idea to provide dried cuttlefish for this purpose, as is commonly done for canaries and budgerigars. Most pet shops sell it.

Calls

The question is often asked - how noisy are quail? As with all things, only a relative answer is possible. As a generalization, males are noisier than females, which confine themselves to subdued little chirrups and soft 'tic-tics' or cooings. The male Coturnix has a rasping chirrupping crow, rather like the harsh cry of the magpie, and is altogether louder and more penetrating. The photograph on page 14 shows a Tuxedo Coturnix male adopting the characteristic upright stance and open-beaked expression when letting the world know of his whereabouts.

The Bobwhite male is also loud, but I do not find his call quite as aggravating as that of the Coturnix. It is basically a three-note, full-bodied piping sound. The female has a quieter version of the same call, with more of a tendency to chirrup.

The Chinese Painted male has a melodious, rather wistful piping whistle. It is almost minor-key, with an evocative atmosphere of the jungle in it. The female is quiet, apart from the occasional and busy 'chic-chic' as she darts about looking for insects.

If there is likely to be a problem of near neighbours complaining about 'noise nuisance' (which is a recognised offence in the UK), it may be better to keep Chinese Painteds, or if Coturnix quails are really wanted, to do without the males.

Head banging

Coturnix quail have a tendency to fly straight up and dash their heads on the roof, sometimes causing injury. It is apparent all through the year, but is much more so in the period leading up to the breeding season, when the migratory urge is at its peak. The only way to deal with this is to place netting just below the roof so that they do not hurt themselves.

Preening

Like all birds, quails will preen themselves regularly, often standing in a patch of sunlight to do so. This ritual of cleaning the feathers with the beak is also a sign that the bird is healthy. A quail which does not preen itself, but has a tendency to stand, looking morose, should be checked, because it is a sure sign that all is not well.

Taming

As a general rule, males should be kept separate to avoid fighting and inter-breeding, but on a small-scale, where there is less pressure of numbers and general stress, they may live together quite happily without fighting. On a small scale, birds do become tame.

I frequently allowed up to seven different males to share the same aviary and concrete run in the summer, with occasional browsing periods on grass in a movable run. In winter, they were housed in canary breeding cages in the conservatory, but were frequently released to enjoy the freedom of the conservatory.

I did not let them inter-breed of course. When I wanted to collect eggs for incubation purposes, I confined the male and females of a particular breed together and kept them separate from the others until I could be sure that the eggs were pure.

I must emphasize that my birds were probably demonstrating behaviour different from the norm, because they were so tame. They knew me and were used to being stroked, talked to and would often take food from my hand. On sunny winter days, I often worked at a table in the conservatory. One or more of the quail would fly up and see what I was doing, often settling down and going to sleep a few inches away. The photograph on page 18 shows an American Range quail on the table. As a matter of interest, there is an American book called 'That Quail, Robert', by Margaret Stranger which is a fascinating account of how the author tamed a Bobwhite

Coping with the head bangers

Plastic or string netting protects the birds from banging their heads on the roof

↑
Quail flies straight upwards

13

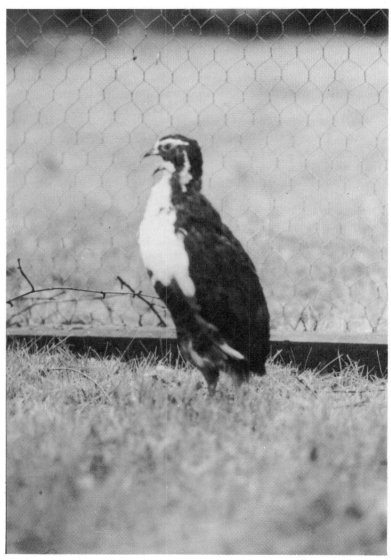

Tuxedo variety of Coturnix laying quail. Note the upright stance of the male when he is calling.

Breeds

If we 'place' the quail in its relative position in the bird world, it is found in the order of *Galliformes*. This is a group which includes game birds and domestic fowl, but not waterfowl. Narrowing the classification further, it is a member of the *Phasianidae* family, a category it shares with pheasants and partridges.

Class: AVES (Birds)

Order: GALLIFORMES (Game birds and Fowl)

Family: TETRAONIDAE   *Family*: PHASIANIDAE

Grouse   Ptarmigan   Capercaillie   Pheasants   Partridges   Quail

Within the quail group, there are fourteen sub-groupings as indicated:

QUAIL
- Anurophasis species
- Callipepla species
- Colinus species
- Coturnix species
- Cyntonyx species
- Dactylortyx species
- Dendrortyx species
- Excalfactoria species
- Odontophorus species
- Ophrysia species
- Oreortyx species
- Perdicula species
- Philortyx species

Each of these sub-groupings has one or more representative species and some of these species also have sub-species, demonstrating the genetic diversification in different geographical locations. There are over forty species of quail in the world, with more than twenty currently being bred in captivity. *The Quail Group of The World Pheasant Association* has an on-going survey of what breeds are being bred, providing valuable recordings for conservation work in this field.

Sub-groupings of quail

Anurophasis monorthonyx		— Snow Mountain quail
Callipepla californica (Lophortyx californica)		— Californian quail
	C. douglasii	— Elegant quail
	C. gambelii	— Gambel's quail
	C. squamata	— Scaled quail
Colinus cristatus		— Crested Bobwhite quail
	C. nigrogularis	— Blackthroated Bobwhite quail
	C. virginianus	— Bobwhite quail
Coturnix coromandelica		— Rail quail
	C. coturnix	— Common, European,
	(C. communis)	Eurasian or Pharoah quail
	C. delegrouei	— Harlequin quail
	C. japonica	— Japanese quail
Cyntonyx montizumae		— Mearns quail
	C. ocellatus	— Ocellated quail
Dactylortyx thoracicus		— Singing quail
Dendrortyx barbatus		— Bearded Tree quail
	D. leucophrys	— Buffycrowned Tree quail
	D. macroura	— Longtailed Tree quail
Excalfactoria chinensis		— Chinese Painted quail
Odontophorus atrifrons		— Blackfronted Wood quail
	O. balliviani	— Stripefaced Wood quail
	O. capueira	— Spotwinged Wood quail
	O. columbianus	— Venezualan Wood quail
	O. dialencos	— Tacaruna Wood quail
	O. erythrops	— Rofousfronted Wood quail
	O. gujanensis	— Marbled quail
	O. guttatus	— Spotted Wood quail
	O. hyperythrus	— Chestnut Wood quail
	O. leucolaemux	— Whitethroated Wood quail
	O. melanonotus	— Darkbacked Wood quail
	O. speciosus	— Rufousfronted Wood quail
	O. stellatus	— Starred Wood quail
	O. strophium	— Gorgeted Wood quail
Ophrysia superciliosa		— Indian Mountain quail
Oreortyx picta		— Mountain quail
Perdicula argoondah		— Rock Bush quail
	P. asiatica	— Jungle Bush quail
	P. erythrorhyncha	— Painted Bush quail
	P. manipurensis	— Manipur Bush quail
Philortyx fasciatus		— Banded quail
Rhynchortyx cinctus		— Tawnyfaced quail

The table above shows the fourteen sub-groupings of the quail family. Each one , such as Coturnix, Colinus or Oreortyx, has one or more species. These, in turn, may have their own sub-species, such as different colour varieties.

Common European Quail
Coturnix coturnix (wild species)

Coturnix Laying Quail
Coturnix coturnix japonica
(Developed strain)

Chinese Painted Quail
Excalfactoria chinensis

Bobwhite Quail
Colinus virginianus

Californian Quail
Callipepla californica

Mountain Quail
Oreortyx picta

Some breeds of quails

Wood Quail (Starred variety)
Odontophorus stellatus

Size

Quail vary in size, from the largest, Longtailed Tree Quail, *Dendrortyx macroura*, at nearly 14", to the smallest, Chinese Painted quail, *Excalfactoria chinensis*, at just over 4". They are found in a wide range of climates, but all share similar characteristics of being shy, quick and with a tendency to hide in ground cover such as long grass or other vegetation.

Life span

There is little information available on this aspect, but Altman and Ditmer, in their report, *Growth including reproduction and morphological development. 1962 (USA)* say that the record life span of a quail is ten years.

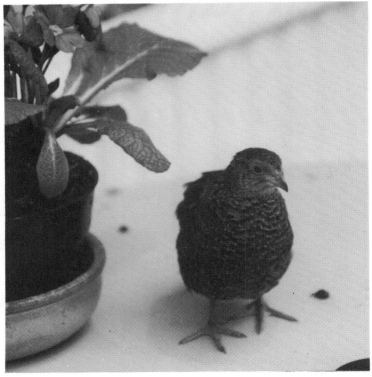

American Range variety of Coturnix quail. Note the large feet in comparison with its size, adapted for scratching the earth for insectivorous food.

Coturnix quail

This is the most common type in captivity worldwide. It is essentially the same bird that the Ancient Egyptians knew and that Mrs. Beeton would have recognised as one of the *'feathered game which have from time immemorial given gratification to the palate of man'*. When reference is made to 'quail' in general, this is the bird in question. In Europe, it has been known as Common quail, European quail and Mediterranean quail. The Old English country name was *Wet-my-lips*, a reference to its familiar call. Pharoah's quail is linked with its Egyptian origins, while in the USA, early settlers referred to it as *German quail*, no doubt because German settlers brought it with them. Eurasian quail is a reminder of its considerable geographical distribution.

Quails have been developed and to a certain extent domesticated, although the word 'domesticated' is used advisedly for they are still essentially 'wild' in their form and behaviour. Although selective breeding has taken place to produce egg laying strains or birds more suited to the table, the development is nowhere near as marked as it is with domestic fowl.

No-one can know for certain how the various breeds and sub-species developed, but it is generally acknowledged that the Coturnix types are based on the Common European quail, *Coturnix coturnix*, Pharoah or Eurasian quail, *Coturnix communis*, and more recently, Japanese quail, *Coturnix japonica*. This was first recognised in the nineteenth century as a separate breed in the wild, but in recent years, the Japanese have developed more productive commercial strains which are also called Japanese quail. Selectively bred laying strains developed from *C. coturnix*, *C. communis* and *C. japonica* are often impossible to distinguish. For convenience, it is easier to refer to them merely as Coturnix laying quail. In America however, they tend to call Coturnix layers, Pharoah quail. In Japan they understandably call them Japanese quail. In Britain where, as always we compromise to try and keep everyone happy, we call them *all* these things. It can be most confusing!

They are basically the same. The male grows to a maximum of 6.5", while the female is slightly larger at an average of 7.5". Both sexes have dappled dark brown, buff and cream striated backs, paler underbellies, breast and flanks. In the female, the markings are less pronounced, while the male's chest is reddish brown. This particular feature enables sex identification to take place at around 3 weeks of age. Before then, it is extremely difficult to do so.

In both sexes there is a distinctive light stripe above each eye, and a white collar, although these may be diminished or even lacking in the female. The beak is yellow-brown to dark olive-brown, the legs pinkish yellow and the eyes dark brown.

The Coturnix laying quail (whether called Japanese or Pharoah) has been selectively bred for commercial production to a limited extent, and the breeders have, in turn, given their own names to particular strains. In the UK, for example, *Curfew* have developed their own *Crusader* strains, while in the USA, *Marsh Farms* produced *Marsh Pharoah* strains.

Coloured varieties of Coturnix

As well as the normal or commercial type of Coturnix laying quail, there are several varieties which show distinct colour variations and markings.

Manchurian quail

The alternative name for these is Manchurian Golden because of their colouring. They are essentially the same breed as the Japanese or Pharoah, but have been developed as a separate variety with golden colouring. Although the markings are the same, the overall hue is lighter and more golden.

American Range

The overall colouring is dark brown, so that some people refer to them as Brown quail. This is a mistake however, for the Brown quail is the name normally given to the Australian breed, *Synoicus ypsilophous*, which is bigger and more greyish in appearance. However, there is a similarity and it is certainly possible that the early Australian settlers introduced the Common quail to that Continent, with subsequent isolated development producing apparently different species.

The markings of the American Range are essentially a lighter brown body colour overlaid with darker-brown, almost black pencilling, along with a certain amount of dark grey feathering on the back. The latter is a point of comparison with the Australian Brown quail.

In America, the Range Coturnix is referred to as the British Range, while in the UK, we call it the American Range!

The overall appearance is dark-brown while the striped head markings are similar to other Coturnix breeds. However, the white eyebrow stripe and white throat markings are absent. Beak and legs are olive-brown and eyes, dark brown,

Fawn quail

This is the variety shown on the outside front cover and is one of my favourites. Essentially like all the other Coturnix breeds, the overall impression of the Fawn is a lovely warm pinkish-brown. The fawn feathers are pencilled with white and the white eyebrow lines are present, although not as strongly defined as in other breeds. Beak and legs are light pinkish-brown, while the eyes are dark brown.

There is no colour difference between the sexes, although as in other breeds, the female is slightly bigger than the male.

English White

Good specimens of these are completely white, with no discernible markings, other than the merest hint of eyebrow lines on the head. It is common, however, to have odd patches of black, and a look at the photograph on the next page indicates that mine do have slight markings on the back of the head. Breeders who are aiming for perfect, all-white specimens can breed this out with careful selective breeding. Beak and legs are pinkish brown and eyes are dark brown.

Male and female are identical, although the female grows to a larger size, particularly noticeable once breeding starts.

Tuxedo

This is an apt name for a bird with a smart white waistcoat to contrast with its dark brown overcoat. The colour of the back feathers is identical with those of the American Range, indicating the close connection with that variety as well as with the English White.

The ideal markings are clear white face, chest and belly, with brown back, tail and crown. In good specimens, the brown and white feathering is neatly demarcated, but it is common to find patches of white where the brown should be, and vice versa. If you look at the photograph on page 14 you will see that one of my Tuxedos has a white splash on the left side of his head, and has brown cheeks instead of white.

Commercial producers of eggs and table quail will tend to concentrate on the straight Coturnix laying strains bred by commercial breeders. On a smaller scale, there is no reason why the interested reader should not go in for the coloured variations of Coturnix. They are often prettier and are usually good egg producers. Egg production levels can, of course, be increased by selective breeding, and it is really the particular strain which is relevant in this respect. In addition to the normal Coturnix laying quail, I have kept American Range, English White, Fawn and Tuxedo. The first do lay more than the others but the difference is not that marked and would only be unacceptable in a commercial egg production unit. On a small scale, many breeders find that concentrating on the coloured varieties is not only more interesting, but they are able to sell breeding pairs or trios of stock in addition to, or instead of eggs.

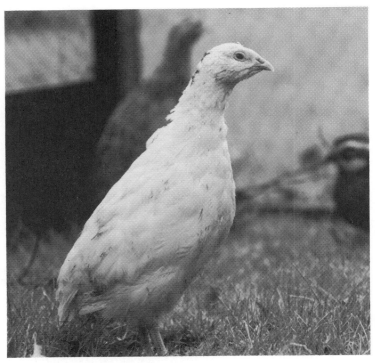

English White variety of Coturnix laying quail

Bobwhite quail

The Bobwhite quail, *Colinus virginianus*, is a breed which has its distribution mainly in North and Central America. Alternative names are American or Partridge quail. The latter name is an appropriate one for it is much more like a partridge than a quail.

There are over twenty sub-species, such as the Masked Bobwhite, *Colinus v. ridgwayi*, a breed currently on the endangered species list.

The breed most commonly kept in captivity is the Common Bobwhite, *Colinus virginianus*. In Britain, it is regarded as an aviary bird. In the USA it is a game bird in the wild, an aviary bird on a small scale and, on a larger scale, is often kept as a commercial egg producer or table bird.

The Bobwhite is a bigger bird altogether than the Coturnix layer, with the male reaching 9.5" and female 10.5". For this reason, it is generally regarded more as a meat bird than an egg producer.

The back, tail and crown of both sexes is dark brown, while the chest, belly and flanks are lighter, with black and white striations. A white stripe covers the eyebrows and, in the male, there is a white patch under the chin. In some females, this patch is absent or reduced, being replaced by buff markings. The overall colour effect is less bright in the female. The beak is greyish-brown, legs yellowish-brown and eyes dark brown,

The Bobwhite is a most attractive bird. I kept a pair in an aviary and they proved to be easy to tame as I have already mentioned. They have a greater tendency to fly and perch than other breeds of quail, so they really need perching facilities.

They can sometimes prove to be aggressive with smaller breeds, but I never found this to be so with mine which cohabited quite happily with Chinese Painted quail and some of the coloured varieties of Coturnix. I should emphasize however, that I kept relatively small numbers of each breed, and succeeded in taming my breeding stock to the extent that they would come when called.

Anyone keeping larger numbers, or on a commercial basis, would obviously keep them separate, and would have less time for conversations.

The Bobwhite quail, a breed indigenous to the American continent.

Ornamental breeds of quail

Chinese Painted quail

The Chinese Painted quail, *Excalfactoria chinensis*, is probably the most widely kept of the ornamental aviary breeds. It is easily the prettiest and most colourful, and in recent years has been much utilized as a spider catcher in butterfly houses. Anyone who has ever visited one of the increasing number of butterfly breeding establishments, such as that at Syon Park in Middlesex, will have seen these busy little birds scuttling through the ground vegetation of the greenhouses, beady eyes on the lookout for unwary spiders and ground insects.

Found in China, India, Sri-Lanka, South Africa and Australia, the Chinese Painted quail is also known as the King quail and the Blue Breasted quail, and there are several sub-species.

It is the smallest of all the quail breeds, with the male reaching 4.5" and the female 5". The male is much more

Chinese Painted quail, the smallest breed and a popular choice for the aviary.

colourful than the female, with brown and black flecked back and crown, bluish-grey breast and face, reddish-brown belly and tail feathers and black and white striped chin and throat. The female is mainly a dullish brown with black and white flecks. She has a white patch on the throat, but the black bars on the throat and face are absent. The beak is black in both sexes, eyes brown

There are variations to these basic standards, with a white, silvery-white and fawnish-brown type. The various sub-species also show differences. In recent years, there has been considerable development to produce new mutations, including Pure White, Gold and Silver, Pearled and Pied strains.

The African Blue Breasted quail, *Excalfactoria adansonii*, has the male much darker backed, but with the wings striped chestnut brown and grey.

The Australian King quail, *E. chinensis lineata*, has more strongly marked lines, as the Latin name implies.

Although the Chinese Painted quail and the coloured varieties of Coturnix are often regarded as ornamentals, and frequently kept in aviaries as such, there is also a growing interest in the rarer, more exotic breeds. Two popular choices, in this respect, are the California quail, and the Mountain quail, illustrated on page 17. Both these breeds are notable for the head plumage. That of the Mountain quail sweeps back in a straight line while that of the smaller California quail curves forwards. They adapt well to aviary conditions, but must have winter protection, and need separate accommodation for breeding purposes.

Other exotic breeds which are bred in captivity in the UK include Gambel's quail, Scaled quail, Elegant quail, Harlequin quail, Rain quail, Masked Bobwhite and Crested Bobwhite. Some of these are available only in limited numbers and the price of rarer species can be high. There is also the question of responsibility in relation to rarer species; that no-one should consider taking them on without having regard for the need to maintain or increase numbers by careful breeding. Reference has already been made to the fact that the Masked Bobwhite is currently on the endangered species list, and strenuous efforts are being made to increase its numbers in the wild.

Coturnix quails are at risk from damaging their heads by flying straight up and banging themselves in low-roofed houses and runs.

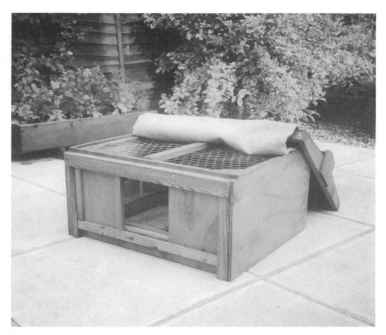

Top: Some of the author's quails. Left to right: Tuxedo, Bobwhite and Fawn.
Bottom: A haybox brooder makes a good house for small quails in an aviary run.
Photo by courtesy of BHT Poultry Housing

Commercial strains of Coturnix quail housed in battery cages in protected housing. Photo by courtesy of *Poultry World.*

Housing

Whatever the housing, it must provide:

- Shelter from the elements
- Adequate warmth and ventilation
- A clean and hygienic environment

The system of housing depends very much on the type and scale of the quail enterprise. A commercial system will be more intensive than that where birds are kept primarily for interest. The more exotic breeds will usually be in aviaries, either indoor or outdoor, with attached house. A small-scale enterprise may utilise small houses and runs. Whichever system is used, the salient point is that quail are not winter hardy and will need adequate housing.

Most commercial enterprises will use either a cage system or a floor-rearing one. The former is where purpose-made cages, equipped with automatic watering facilities are used. The latter is where a building with a concrete floor is furnished with wood shavings, feeders and drinkers, and the birds can roam at will within the confines of the house.

A concrete floor is essential, and the building needs to be substantial enough, not only to deter rodents but also to provide draught-free and well-ventilated, sheltered accommodation.

Ventilation by roof ridge and side window is ideal, as a through current of fresh air is provided. The arrangement of this will vary depending on the type of house. Very large houses will use fans.

Lighting in a house is not only necessary for efficient management, but it will also provide a stimulus for winter eggs, although table birds should not be given extra light.

Heating in winter is not necessary as long as there is adequate insulation. This can be in the form of insulation boards purchased from a DIY centre and hammered onto the inside roof and walls. Alternatively, a relatively new technique is to spray insulation on the walls and roof.

Newly-hatched quail will naturally have localised heat in the form of brooder lamps until they are hardy.

As there is so much variation in the types and scale of possible housing, it is a good idea at this point, to take a more detailed look at the various options.

Cage systems

Cages are used by most commercial units where eggs are being produced. Some people dislike cages on humanitarian grounds, but there are also 'deep-litter' type cages available in addition to the normal type. *Curfew* supplies both kinds.

Quail cages can be stacked on top of each other, to an overall height of 6'3". Each unit has a drop-tray for ease of cleaning, and feeders and drinkers are provided at the ends and sides of the cages. Automatic watering in the form of header tank, pipes and clips can provide a round-the-clock supply of fresh water.

These particular cages can be used in association with *Curfew* tiered brooders. Quail chicks can then be raised from day-olds in the brooders until they are three weeks old when the brooders are switched off. The brooder area and run can then be used for the main runs.

The cages are 20" x 24" x 11" high. Each cage comes fitted with a feeder, and manually filled or automatic drinkers are easily fitted. The floor is plastic covered mesh which is easy on the feet, and eggs as they are laid, roll forward for collection. The cages can be stacked four or five high and there is a removable droppings tray beneath each one. Each cage, in theory, can hold 15 quail, but it is not necessary to have as many as that.

In summer, each cage can be lifted out quite easily and placed on grass in a sheltered area so that the quail have access to the grass which comes up through the mesh. One producer I met does this regularly, placing her 30 cages outside, on a different area each day so that it keeps down the grass in her adjoining field. The cages have a windbreak in the form of a line of straw bales placed in the way of the prevailing wind. If the weather is particularly windy, cold or wet, the cages are left inside, This practice, according to the owner, is a reasonable compromise, for she shares my dislike of batteries in general, but can see the value of them if used with a little imagination. The supplier of the cages confirmed that several producers use his cages in this way; adding that most quail producers are in fact, small scale, and prefer to utilise small scale practices.

It is also possible to make your own cages, of course, and welded mesh is the most suitable material. A protective strip

A system of indoor rabbit hutches adapted by the author to provide quail housing. The covered areas provide sleeping accommodation while the wire mesh on the roof of the living area allows adequate light to enter to ensure winter egg production.

wooden floor   wooden wall   mesh attached to outside of wall

weldmesh panel set in floor

A droppings panel set into the floor of a wooden hutch facilitates cleaning

for the edges of cut welded mesh is available by the metre, from cage suppliers such as *Curfew*.

Some people prefer to make their own cages using a wooden framework. Other alternatives are to adapt rabbit hutches or wooden bird breeding cages.

The use of wire bottoms for the cages facilitates cleaning and prevents a possible build-up of disease, but does mean that the birds are unable to scratch in the way they do in unrestricted conditions. For this reason, some quail breeders prefer to use wooden bird breeding cages, with solid wooden floors, sides and roofs, and a mesh cage front. These require a greater degree of management, because the wood shavings floor litter does need to be cleared out regularly. However, these wooden cages are usually equipped with a sliding floor section so that cleaning is not that great a task. A section of weldmesh panel can also be inserted in one area of the floor to facilitate cleaning. I adapted a bank of rabbit hutches in this way and they worked well in an outhouse.

Young quail being raised on a floor system in protected housing.
Photo by courtesy of Poultry World.

Floor systems

A floor-system is set up inside a building where the door has an interior flight entrance. This is essentially to stop birds escaping when you open the door, and works on the 'air-lock' principle. In other words, you close the outside door before opening the interior one. It need not necessarily be a door; it could be strips of wood or wire mesh strategically placed to provide a barrier. Quails are great escapers and it is not worth trying to adapt a floor-system house for them unless an interior flight door is incorporated.

Concrete floors really are essential for such a system, for rats are highly intelligent and devious in their efforts to gain entry into an area where there are vulnerable young birds.

Wood shavings provide the best litter material. They are clean, absorbent and also absorb smells. Suspended feeders and drinkers are probably best in this sort of situation, for they are less likely to have litter scratched into them.

A less intensive floor-system for those who like to give their birds more freedom, is one which has the inside run extending outside. An example is shown in the illustration on page 35. Here, the birds range on the concrete floor with wood shavings inside the house and also on a concrete run outside, via a pop-hole. Again, concrete is a good idea here, not only because the run is rat-proof, but droppings can be swept with a broom, and if necessary, hosed down when the birds are confined inside by closing the pop-hole. Naturally, woodshavings are not used in the outside run, but it may be a good idea to provide a shallow, dustbath area of fine sand so that they can take dustbaths in fine weather.

The outside run is enclosed by stout wire mesh of a gauge too fine to allow rodents to enter and the bottom section has protective boards which help to protect against the wind. It is about 3' high with a gate for human access, making run clearance easier.

The provision of a certain amount of natural cover will be welcomed by the birds. Terry Rolph, the breeder of *Crusader* Coturnix quail, tells me that some conifer branches placed in one corner are suitable, or conifer trees in pots. Bracken cuttings and various logs have also been used to good effect. Even if the run is completely contained within a building, the provision of such cover is appreciated.

Here an 'open house' system is used, where all the birds are in the same area. The porch with its external and internal door prevents any escapes and also provides extra draught protection when the outside door is opened. Artificial lighting to supply a total of 16 hours of natural/artificial light is necessary for layers. Table birds do not need artificial light otherwise growth is slowed down.

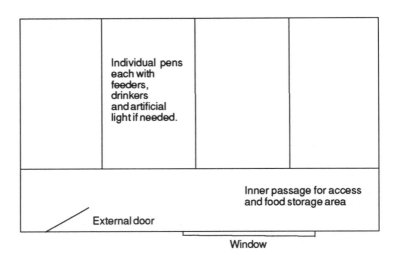

Here the area is divided into several pens with access from an internal passage which not only acts as a porch, but also doubles as a food storage area.

Two ways of using a building for a floor system of rearing

A series of interlocking posts and game netting can be used to make internal pens in a building where a floor system is in use. This simplifies management and prevents mass panic when the birds crowd in the same direction at the same time. It can also be used to make internal divisions in an aviary, as well as temporary outside pens in the summer. Another application is as an internal door in a floor system building, preventing birds escaping when the main door is opened. Photos by courtesy of *Agriframes Ltd.*

A less intensive floor system where quails have access to an outside run via a pop-hole

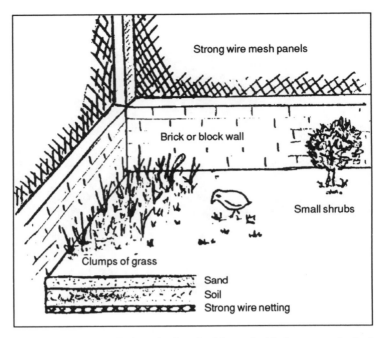

An outside run for hardier breeds of quails. A house inside the run, or attached to it will still be necessary

A small aviary built onto a conservatory, allowing both winter and summer accomodation

Aviary systems

Quail breeders and keepers of ornamental or rarer species of quail often use an aviary system. The simplest of these is the small house with attached run, or a bank of these arranged in such a way that the individual runs are parallel with each other, but separate, so that different breeds are kept apart. It is normal for specific breeds to be kept in pairs or trios, but several pairs should not normally be kept together because the males may fight. Hen birds of the same variety can usually be housed together.

There are many purpose-built aviaries available from specialist suppliers, and they can be most attractive, particularly in a garden setting.

Many breeders, particularly of the more ornamental varieties, like to have runs with natural vegetation. It is possible to arrange this, as long as precautions to deter rats are taken. I have already referred to the fact that concrete runs are the safest, but strong wire mesh laid on the ground and extending beyond the perimeter is a good alternative. Once in position, rubble is placed on top, followed by soil and a layer of sand. Small shrubs or other plants can then be planted directly into the soil. Long grasses are particularly suitable for they emulate the conditions which many breeds of quail frequent in the wild. As long as there is a quiet, protected corner with such plants, many quail breeds will build nests and incubate their eggs. The Chinese Painted quail, for example, will make a nest in the middle of a clump of long grass, while Coturnix breeds will also become broody, particularly in their second year.

It is necessary to sound a note of warning about the type of netting used underneath the soil in runs such as this, I once used netting which was slightly rusty. I reasoned that it was not good enough for anything else but was quite suitable for putting under the soil. It was a grave error! Rats discovered a weak point and burrowed under the perimeter wall, coming straight up in the centre of the run. They killed the three Japanese quail, one male and two females, who were residents.

A really rat-proof floor is provided by using flag stones instead of netting. These placed close together will exclude even the most devious of rats, while the cracks between them will provide necessary drainage. Rubble, soil and finally sand can then be placed on top as before. Sand is recommended

Two types of aviary for keeping quail and other ornamental birds. Photos by courtesy of Shropshire Bird and Aquatic Centre because it does allow the birds to make their own dust-bathing depressions, as well as providing a popular scratching area. Some breeders recommend this also as a means of deterring earthworms from coming to the surface. Earth-worms are hosts to a number of parasites which can be transmitted to quail.

An outside aviary run of this type also needs protective walls at the base, with wire mesh above. The ideal, particularly for smaller quail such as the Chinese Painted which can escape through small crevices, is a solid wall five to six horizontal brick level high. This also provides wind and draught protection.

Within such an aviary any stout house which is rain and draught-proof is suitable. In milder areas of the country, hardier breeds of quail can be left in outdoor runs, as long as their houses are well insulated. In more exposed areas, many breeders transfer their breeding stock to breeding cages inside a shed or aviary house, moving them out again in spring. This practice allows time for a good winter clean up of the outdoor aviaries, as well as a time for doing any necessary repairs. It is good practice, at this time, to sprinkle some lime on the empty run - just enough to give the impression of a light dusting of snow. It helps to clear the ground of any residual pests which may cause disease. The ground itself also has time to recover before the birds are returned to their summer quarters. Some breeders remove the top few inches of soil and replace it with fresh soil.

One of the nicest aviary systems I have seen was built half in and half out of a conservatory. During the spring, summer and autumn, the quail, which in this case were Chinese Painteds, were able to move from the inside aviary to the outside one by means of a sliding door partition at the base. The aviary was a tall one which also housed canaries, They too had a sliding door partition, higher up on the dividing wall, and had access to the outside run when conditions were suitable.

Chinese Painted quail are frequently kept in aviaries where tree perching birds are kept because they help to clear up the seeds dropped by the flying birds. This should not be regarded as the sole source of food for them however. It is not enough for they need a properly balanced diet like any other species. (See the section on Feeding.) In this context, I should mention a lady who kept Java finches, her prime interest. She had introduced several Chinese Painted quail into the bottom of the aviary because s.omeone had told her they were useful to clean up aviary floors. She telephoned me to say that they *'kept dying'* and did I know why? During the course of the conversation it emerged that not only did they have no food other than what the finches left, but had no house or any form of shelter other than the sapling which was planted in the aviary. Yet the Java finches had a proper diet and sheltered accommodation. No wonder they kept dying, the poor things!

Chinese Painted quail are ground-orientated birds and need to have proper rations and clean water provided for them in suitable containers on the ground, rather than having to rely on the occasional spilt seeds falling like manna from above. They also need proper housing which will provide warmth and shelter, free of damp and draughts. A fairly simple house is all that is necessary, but it should have woodshavings or other warm nesting material to provide insulation.

The movable house and run

If small numbers of quails are to be kept outside an aviary or house, the best solution is to use a strong house and run of the type used by poultry keepers for hens and chicks. These can be moved from one area of grass to another, allowing them access to clean pasture on a regular basis. The house needs a well boarded floor capable of deterring rats, so that once shut up for the night the birds are safe from harm. The run which has a wire floor resting on the grass, is obviously safer than the floorless type.

With such a system, it is a good idea to keep specific breeds together, rather than mix them up, although females of the various Coturnix varieties will cohabit successfully. Males housed together may fight and should, as a rule, be kept separate from each other. One male can usually accompany up to around half a dozen females, although it is worth remembering that Chinese Painted quail are monogamous and normally kept in pairs.

Remember again, that quail are not naturally hardy birds. While a small house and run may be satisfactory in the warmer months, it is not usually successful in winter. My own practice is to have the birds in a house and run in summer and then to transfer them to indoor breeding cages for the winter. I find it safer to put the runs on concrete rather than on grass, not only because they are safer from predators, but also to minimise the risk of infection from droppings. They have a box of sand in which to make dust baths, and some branches placed to provide shade and slightly more natural conditions. They do occasionally go on grass however, as the photograph below shows.

It is possible, in milder areas of the country, to have quails in outdoor houses and runs in winter, but even in such areas of Britain, recent winters have been severe, and I would advise against it. Having said that, I have heard of a lady in Sussex who has a few quail completely free-ranging in her back garden all through the year. I wonder how she coped in recent, severe winters.

Some of the author's quails in a small movable run on grass. This is temporary accommodation, giving them access to grass during warm summer days.

Design for a small quail house and run

Roof overhangs part of run to give added rain and wind protection

4'

House door

Ventilation window

½" gauge wire mesh for run

Run door

Pop-hole

Flat wooden rails allowing house to be pulled easily to a new site

Strong ½" wire mesh for rat-proof floor to run, but allows grass to get through

Internal netting can be erected to prevent head banging on the roof. If insulation is adequate, laying quail can over-winter here, but they need artificial light, not only to produce winter eggs, but to keep active for longer periods, thus generating warmth.

The author's male and female Japanese strain of Coturnix quails in an outside concrete run which has an attached house.

Feeding

Quail need a 27% protein ration when they are growing, with a reduced percentage once they are fully grown. There are ready formulated commercial quail feeds, but they are fairly expensive. Many large producers make up their own feeds, buying in the appropriate ingredients from their local mill. A favourite mixture is as follows:

6 parts turkey crumbs: 1 part pheasant crumbs

Smaller units, particularly those operating on an aviary basis, make up their own rations using a wider variety of ingredients, and including grain. Such a formula might be:

1 part oatmeal: 1 part chick crumbs: 1 part millet:
1 part shelled canary seed

Aviary feed specialists normally stock a range of mixtures, including 'quail mixtures'. Although the ingredients tend to be the same, the proportions in relation to each other may be different.

As far as my own quail are concerned, I make up a mixture as follows:

1 part chick crumbs: 1 part canary seed: 1 part millet

In addition to this, they have surplus lettuce leaves, and outer leaves from kitchen garden vegetables. They also have access to grit which is, of course, essential where grain is given, for the proper functioning of the crop in breaking down and digesting seeds. I should make it clear that while this feeding pattern is ideal for rearing healthy, lively quail on a small scale, it would not be practicable or realistic for a large unit.

It is worth mentioning that for the chicks of Chinese Painted quail even chick crumbs may prove to be too coarse for the first few days. I grind some up to make it finer for them, but it is only necessary to do this for about a week.

Another point worth making is that some feed manufacturers now produce a 28% protein pheasant ration which could be suitable for quail, if the price is reasonable. It is worth enquiring at your local mill or feed supplier. Also, ask about chick crumbs without coccidiostats, for it is obviously not a good idea to give feed which has antiobiotic additives on a permanent basis.

Perhaps one of the most unusual quail diets I have come

A range of Feeding and Drinking equipment suitable for quails

Suspended feeder

Open feeder - liable to have food scratched out of it

Examples of feeders where it is not as easy to scratch out the food

Hopper type feeder

'Parrot' feeder for attaching to cage

Automatic drinkers for use with a header tank

across is that adopted by a contributor to *Home Farm* magazine who lives in a New York apartment. He rears quails in a range of old fish tanks and also raises earthworms and catfish. He mixes his feed in a 30 gallon capacity bucket, using a trowel as a scoop, and his formula is as follows:

Half a scoop alfalfa meal: 1 scoop mixed dried roots, seeds and leaves: 1 scoop chopped wheat sprouts: 1 tablespoon iodized salt: 1 tablespoon ground limestone

This is supplemented with surplus baby catfish, live worms and freshly shredded greens. The New York diet certainly ensures that the quail have enough protein, but there would be few people dedicated enough to follow it.

Feed equipment

Quail are inveterate scratchers and will propel their food in all directions if given the opportunity to do so. Those in commercial cage systems will probably have external feed troughs so that only the head can reach them. Where a floor system is used, suspended feeders which are clear of the ground are the most suitable. If they are gravity-fed or hopper type feeders, the surface area presented to the bird is small enough to prevent jumping up and scratching, yet gravity fills up the feeding area as the feed is eaten.

I have found that using flat open containers is a waste of time. The quail merely jump in and scratch the food everywhere. One might as well put it all on the floor in the first place. If the birds are in a concrete run, and the weather is dry, then adopting this latter course is suitable. A concrete run can be kept clean easily by sweeping and hosing down.

Commercially, feed is available at all times, with the birds helping themselves from the feed troughs on an ad-lib basis. Each adult quail will consume about 4½ oz a week. On a smaller scale, feeding twice a day is enough, as long as sufficient feed is given. With my rule-of-thumb approach, I find that one of my handfuls (I have small hands) is enough for six quail at a time, and I feed morning and afternoon. This is a fairly general estimate of course, and there are bound to be variations. Some birds naturally eat more than others, while temperature fluctuations will also have a bearing on consumption: they eat more in winter in order to keep warm.

Water

Clean water is essential at all times and there is no question of making this available a couple of times a day. It must be there whenever the birds feel like drinking, which could be anytime. Again, a commercial unit will normally have an automatic system which utilizes a header tank, tubing, connectors and the drinkers themselves. In a floor system, suspended drinkers as part of an automatic system work well.

On a smaller scale, suspended drinkers which operate on a gravity-principle are satisfactory. This is the type I use for my quail, and I find that refilling once a day is enough to ensure a supply of water for 24 hours. When my quails are brought inside to their wooden canary breeding cages for the winter, I use parrot drinkers. These clip onto the bars of the front of the cage and one of these is enough for a pair of birds for 24 hours. I should add that, in these circumstances, I have no choice but to use flat open dishes for their food, and have to put up with a certain amount of food scratching and dispersal.

Grit

Although a proprietary mixture such as the turkey crumb/pheasant crumb mixture, referred to on page 43, is said to be a balanced diet without the need of extra grit, I have my reservations about this. It has always been my experience that birds need a small amount of extra grit, and I prefer to err on the side of caution by making it available to them. If grains such as millet, or chopped wheat are given then grit is absolutely essential otherwise the crop which is responsible for grinding up the grain particles cannot function properly.

On a commercial scale, where feed may be made available on a conveyor system, the grit can be incorporated into the feed at the mixing stage. On a smaller scale, the odd handful given separately on the ground about once a week is sufficient. Fine grit suitable for quail is available from most pet-shops or aviary suppliers. Branded supplies usually contain added minerals which help to keep the stock healthy. Grit supplied by poultry suppliers for chickens may prove to be too coarse for quail.

If cuttlefish is provided for beak care, this may also provide sufficient grit and calcium for the digestive system.

Green food

I have already referred to the fact that my quail have kitchen garden surpluses such as overblown lettuce. They quickly shred their way through such leaves with their sharp beaks, and it is arguable that this activity has a beneficial effect in preventing feather pecking or other aggressive behaviour, rather than the strictly nutritional benefits. Most commercial quail would not have access to green food, although it is my belief that quail are healthier, happier and longer-lived when they have a good basic diet with lots of variety. If it is true for humans, then why not for quails?

Fawn Coturnix quail in a movable run on grass

THE ESSENTIALS OF INCUBATION

TEMPERATURE — 37.7°C (100°F) in centre of egg
HUMIDITY — 65%. Increase to 70% 2 days before hatch
TURNING — 5 times a day

Good, healthy and unrelated breeding stock with proven performance

Store fertile eggs at 14.5°C with blunt end up, and at angle of 45°. Reverse the direction of tilt twice daily. Incubate before 7 days old.

Incubate at temperature of 39.4°C (103°F) when the thermometer is 2" above the centre of the eggs in a still air thermometer. The temperature in the middle of the egg should not exceed 37.7°C (100°F).
Follow the manufacturer's instructions!

If incubator does not have an automatic turning facility, turn the eggs five times a day. Wash your hands before handling them.

The humidity should be 65% for most of the incubation period, increasing to 70% for the last 2 days before hatching.

wooden box — hole 28mm (1⅛ in) in diameter

60 watt bulb

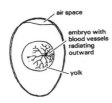

air space

embryo with blood vessels radiating outward

yolk

After hatching, wait until the chicks are dry and fluffed up before moving to protected brooding conditions with food and water.

INCUBATION TIMES

Coturnix breeds	18 days
Bobwhite breeds	23 days
Chinese Painted	16 days

(These are average times - they may vary by a couple of days each way)

Candle after 6-7 days if you must to see which eggs are fertile and which are not developing.

Breeding

Breeding is an essential aspect of keeping quail, whether on a large or a small scale. Large production units in the UK tend to breed and rear their own replacement breeding stock, rather than buy in 'point-of-lay' stock, as is the case in the poultry world. The reason for this is because the selective breeding of quail has not taken place to the same degree as it has with poultry. As I have already mentioned, there are some large breeders who selectively breed and sell commercial strains but it is still not a widespread practice. Most producers find that it is better to breed their own replacements, buying in new breeders for the breeding flock as and when necessary.

Smaller enterprises, which often have the coloured and ornamental breeds, generally find that breeding such stock has a ready market among interested poultry keepers, rare breed enthusiasts and aviary owners. Whatever the scale, breeding quail has a fascination which few could doubt. I find it the most interesting aspect of all.

The key factor is to obtain good breeding stock to start with, and it is here that a specialist supplier can help. They are listed at the end of the book.

Breeding stock

It goes without saying that the breeding stock should be healthy, have no visible defects and be unrelated. The latter consideration is often overlooked, and purchasers of a pair of a particular breed, may unknowingly have acquired a brother and sister.

Such inbreeding can result in genetic defects being thrown up in the progeny. I once found that a clutch of Japanese Coturnix chicks had three born without claws on the feet. They were the progeny of a pair which I had bought specifically as breeders, although to be fair to the supplier, I did not stress this at the time of purchase. If I had, perhaps the story might have been different. What I should have done, of course, was either to have ensured that they were from different lines, or to have acquired them from different sources. I could also have bought two pairs, one from each source, and swapped over the males.

The use of leg rings is essential in order to keep adequate records and to ensure that you know which bird is which. Normal poultry leg rings are too large, but quail rings are available from specialist suppliers, listed in the reference section. These can be obtained in different colours, and in a numbered sequence if required. They are available in plastic or aluminium.

Before collecting eggs for incubation, the male and females should have been confined together in breeding quarters for at least a week, and it is as well to discard the eggs for incubating for the first few days afterwards (although they should still be collected) until they have settled down into a regular output.

Breeding ratio

Coturnix quail can be kept in pairs, trios or one male for 5 - 6 females.

Bobwhites are normally kept in pairs, although there is no reason why the number of females should not be increased.

Chinese Painted quail are naturally monogamous and should be kept in pairs.

The rarer, ornamental breeds are usually kept in pairs or trios. If you want to keep a precise record of which hen is producing which egg, then the obvious solution is to house only a pair in the breeding quarters. Selective breeding for a particular characteristic is made much easier in this way.

Selective breeding may be for a number of reasons: colour, feather markings, egg production, quick growth, weight - and so on. The basic principle which operates is that if you breed from two birds which both have a similar characteristic, their progeny will tend to have the same feature,

In many commercial units, it is normal to have one male to each four hens in the cages and mixed running is no problem as far as commercial egg sales are concerned. The eggs are collected every morning and graded. The large and the small ones are selected for selling, while the medium-sized ones are retained for incubation. Of those hatched, most will be reared as table birds, while some are retained as future breeders. Stock birds which are eventually selected from these are then housed in trios in separate breeding accommodation.

Above: Closed aluminium rings which are put on when the chicks are a few days old. Marked with the current year, they guarantee the age of the bird. Coturnix quails take size R while Chinese Painted quails take size L.
Illustrations by courtesy of Southern Aviaries.

Right: Plastic split ring available in 12 single colours or 76 striped colours. They are used for the identification of breeding stock and breeding lines. They can be put on at any age with the aid of an opening tool, as shown. Coturnix quails take size 1FB, while Chinese Painteds take size XB.

The onset of lay

Coturnix quail will start to lay at around five weeks old, and the eggs will be fertile from about 6 weeks onwards. The behaviour of the male will leave no doubt as to when the fertile stage is reached because he will produce 'foam balls' and deposit them on the ground.

Once the male is sexually active, he will mate frequently with the females, gripping the feathers on the top of their heads with his beak. The photograph on the next page shows how a certain amount of feather denuding of the head occurs at this time.

Occasionally, the skin is pierced leaving a wound. If this happens, the female should be removed immediately, in case the bloodstain incites aggressive attack. A period in a hospital cage in solitary confinement will soon enable her to recover. Occasionally, a male will object to a particular female for no apparent reason, attacking her in a vicious way. When this happens, there is no other solution but to split them up permanently.

Above: the foam ball of the male bird. Photo: Mark Bomer

Left: Foam ball deposited on the ground. Compare the size with a pound coin.

Below: Female Coturnix showing denuding of the head feathers during the breeding season.

Storing eggs prior to incubation

Once the eggs have been selected for incubation, they should be incubated as soon as possible, and certainly no later than a week after being laid. They need to be stored in a cool room at around 15°C (the optimum is 14.5°C), with the pointed end down. The photograph on page 55 shows this operation in progress in the hatchery of a large commercial quail farm.

The eggs are turned through 45° morning and evening, until they are placed in the incubator. On a small scale they can be placed in cartons, with one end balanced on a brick, while a second brick stops it slipping (as shown below). The carton is tipped in the other direction, at 45°, with the change taking place twice a day.

On a large scale, commercial hatcheries will fumigate or otherwise disinfect their hatching eggs to ensure that they are disease-free. On a small scale this is probably unnecessary but it is still important to wash your hands before handling them and to remember to do so before you turn them in the incubator, if you need to do so manually.

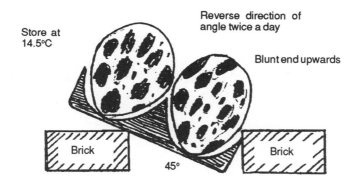

Store at 14.5°C

Reverse direction of angle twice a day

Blunt end upwards

Brick

Brick

45°

Natural incubation

Coturnix quail are not particularly good mothers in captivity, although they will become broody and sit on their own eggs if conditions are acceptable to them. They are more likely to do this in a floor-system or in an aviary, where a certain amount of natural cover and vegetation is present. They can cover about ten eggs at a time. Bantam hens such as Silkies or

Silkie crosses have been used with success to hatch quail, but I have never tried this. In the first issue of this book I asked whether any readers had succeeded in hatching quail by natural methods, and I am pleased to say that I received the following letter from Elaine P. Samson of St. Andrews in Australia:

'One of my Pekin bantams (first time mum) raised six quails without any trouble. She sat on seven eggs and treated them as her own chicks. I kept them in a small pen with very small wire, and used a water drinker of the free standing type which is used for small cage birds. For the feeder I had the base of a drinker which usually holds an upside-down bottle.

Although this is only a one-off experiment, I can't see any reason why it shouldn't work well with any calm type of bantam.

I took 'mum' away at three weeks and moved the quails to an aviary at four weeks.'

Quail chick's toes damaged by underfloor heating in a brooder.

Quails' eggs being set for storage prior to incubation at a commercial hatchery. Photo by courtesy of Poultry World.

Artificial incubation

Most quail are incubated artificially and certainly on a commercial scale, it is essential. Large units will have a separate setting room and incubation room.

On a smaller scale, most general purpose small incubators are satisfactory for quail. I have used a Bristol incubator for a number of years and have had good results for quail, poultry and waterfowl with it. Of course, the eggs have to be turned manually and this is a nuisance when it needs to be done three times, and ideally five times, a day.

A quail breeder in the West Country told me that he had consistently poor hatchings with a manually operated incubator, and when he went over to using an incubator with automatic turning facilities, his problems ceased. Certainly, the small electronic incubator with such a facility is an enormous step forward for the small poultry breeder. The one illustrated overleaf, for example, has egg dividers of varying sizes to cater for a range of different eggs.

Top: A small incubator with automatic turning facilities and adapted for quails' eggs.
Below: Newly hatched quails in a small incubator.
Photos by courtesy of Brinsea Incubators

Regular turning is essential, if the developing embryo is not to stick to one side of the shell membranes, with a resulting malformation. Automatic turning frees one from the chore of having to remember to do this at regular intervals (and how many of us are scrupulous in this?)

It is possible to candle the eggs at around 5 days, in order to discover which eggs are fertile and developing, and which are not. Commercially this is done so that efficient use of incubator space is maximised. On a small scale it is hardly necessary for incubation time is not that long:

- Coturnix   18 days
- Chinese Painted 16 days
- Bobwhites   23 days

I have always found that the speckled nature of quails' eggs makes them quite difficult to candle effectively.

As far as effective overall incubation is concerned, the single most important piece of advice is to follow the individual manufacturer's advice to the letter. He knows his incubator better than anyone else, and will normally give good instructions for different breeds. The subject of incubation is covered in considerable depth in my other book *Incubation: A Guide to Hatching and Rearing*.

Brooding

It is often claimed that your problems with quails only start once they are hatched. Their small size certainly makes them more effective escapees than poultry chicks. A glance at the photograph on page 58 indicates the size of a newly hatched Coturnix quail. That of the Chinese Painted quail is around the size of a bumble bee. Any brooder housing will require finely meshed wire to ensure that they do not escape through the holes. I find that for Chinese Painted quail, an old fish tank with netting across the top is the safest brooder.

For Coturnix chicks I adapted an indoor rabbit hutch to provide heating from a red bulb. This is confined to what had been the rabbit's sleeping accommodation and the presence of wood shavings as litter provides a warm, comfortable area. Food and water are made available in the living accommodation half. I had to replace the existing bars of this section with fine wire mesh. That produced by *Twilweld* and available

Top: A newly hatched Coturnix quail chick
Bottom: The same chick three days later.

from many large garden centres or aviary suppliers is ideal. There are, of course, many possibilities when it comes to making home-made brooders and even a large cardboard box can be turned into an effective brooder.

Commercial brooding units are also available and, on a large scale, a floor system such as that shown on page 32 is ideal. Here, the quail chicks are on wood shavings in a rat-proof building with heat provided by overhead brooding units.

Food is made available in shallow containers or chick feeders which allow the head to enter, but prevent them getting in to scratch out the food.

Small, gravity-fed drinkers are available and the brooding area is confined to the vicinity of the lamps by wire netting lined with plastic feed sacks as insulation.

As the chicks grow and develop, these confining walls are removed and the artificial heat switched off. As a general rule, heat will be necessary for about three weeks, gradually raising the lamps to harden off the young birds.

The outside temperature naturally has an influence, and in particularly cold periods, it may be necessary to extend the period of heating. Similarly, if it is warm, the availability of artificial heat can be reduced or withdrawn earlier.

Table quail will be ready for killing from the age of 6 weeks onwards when they have reached a liveweight of 6-7 oz.

Sexing quail

Coturnix laying quail are easy to sex because from about three weeks onwards, the reddish brown chest of the male will start to become noticeable. His markings are also more distinct and sharp than those of the female. Once they are adult and in breeding condition, from about 6 weeks onwards, the larger size of the female and the sexual behaviour and foam ball production of the male, referred to earlier, will be apparent.

Before the age of 3 weeks, it is virtually impossible to sex the birds, and it is debatable whether it is necessary at this stage anyway.

The same is generally true for other breeds of quail. If there is anyone eagle-eyed and knowledgeable enough to sex the bumble bee sized Chinese Painteds, I shall be interested to know what the secret is!

Infra-red bulb — or ordinary red bulb in small brooder,

Section of front cut away to show the interior.

Food and water.

A home-made brooder for a small number of young quail. It could be an adapted rabbit hutch or a large cardboard box.

Lamp with red bulb

Netting

Old fish tank

Wood shavings litter

Some ideas on brooding young quail. (See page 32 for larger scale or commercial floor system).

Dull—emitter heater suitable for brooding young quail. Illustration by courtesy of George H. Elt Ltd.

The coloured varieties of Coturnix, such as English White, American Range and Tuxedo do not have an apparent difference in feathering between the male and female. The only way to tell them apart is to go by size difference (the female is bigger), by sexual behaviour patterns and by vent examination. In the male this is more domed, while that of the female is more inverted, as shown in the illustration. This difference is only apparent after they have reached sexual maturity, when their behaviour will indicate their sexes anyway.

Also, in adulthood, is the difference in vocal sounds which has been mentioned earlier in the book.

Side view of vent area of male quail

Side view of vent area of female

Problems with young quail

Reference has already been made to the fact that young quail are escapees and that all cracks and crevices must be filled. The gauge of any netting used needs to be no bigger than ½" and that manufactured by *Twilweld* is ideal in this respect.

Their tendency to drown easily in shallow water should also be taken seriously, and for the first week, drinkers need to have clean pebbles or marbles placed in them, so that the depth of water is reduced to a safe level, while still providing water for them to drink.

I have also referred to the effects of inbreeding of parent stock leading to genetic defects, such as my experience of having quail chicks born without claws.

Another problem with feet which I discovered to my cost some years ago was when I used a brooder with under-floor heating. Although equipped with thermostat and having adequate insulation as well as wood shavings litter on top, the whole batch of quail developed the same foot problem. Basically this was a blackening of the toes, followed by rapid withering and ultimately the complete loss of them. The whole batch had to be put down and I have never used this form of brooding again. The problem has never recurred.

Top: Left to right - a chicken's egg, a Coturnix quail egg and a Chinese Painted quail egg. (The photograph is half normal size)

Bottom: Any water container should have pebbles placed in the water to make the depth shallower and prevent drowning

Eggs

Coturnix eggs

The eggs of Coturnix birds are off-white splashed with chocolate brown. The latter may be in the form of tiny spots, large spots or large splodges. There is a considerable variation in patterning.

I once tried to keep a record of all the variations of patterning, hoping that I would be able to identify particular eggs as belonging to specific hens, without having to trap nest. I soon gave up because just when I thought I was getting somewhere, a new variation would appear. They also occasionally produce olive-coloured eggs with no markings at all, just to be perverse. Occasionally, some strains will produce all-white eggs as a mutation. The size is approximately one third that of a chicken's egg (see the photograph opposite!).

In the wild, about a dozen eggs are laid in a clutch, with two or possibly three clutches in a season. Selectively bred strains can produce between 150-200 eggs without artificial light. The provision of light and good winter management can increase this to 200-300 eggs. It should be emphasized, however, that to achieve such production levels requires the use of good commercial strains, and a high level of management.

In Britain, the same Coturnix quail are generally used for egg production as well as for the table trade. Although there has not been widespread selective breeding and development for commercial purposes, as with poultry, it has occurred on a limited basis.

Terry Rolph of *Curfew*, has developed his own 'Crusader' commercial strain, while in the USA, *Marsh Farms* have bred the 'Marsh Pharoah' strains for both eggs and table birds. In Japan, where selective breeding has perhaps been more intensive than anywhere else, various strains of Japanese quail have been developed for eggs, table birds and for laboratory research.

Good commercial strains are therefore available and anyone thinking of starting a quail enterprise, is advised to invest in such stock. Once the enterprise is running smoothly you should also concentrate on doing your own selective breeding, by maintaining a breeding flock from which future quality birds can be selected.

Bobwhite eggs

The eggs are slightly bigger than those of Coturnix breeds, and generally have a paler appearance. The background colour is off-white with a fine speckling of brown spots. There is a variation in patterning, with some eggs having bolder markings than others, but on the whole, they are more finely marked.

In the wild, up to about two dozen eggs are produced in a season. Selectively-bred specimens in protected conditions can produce 50-100 eggs a year, with no extra light. With the provision of artificial light, the provision of winter quarters and adequate feed rations, this can be increased to 150-200 a year.

In the USA, the Bobwhite quail is currently used for egg production to a limited degree, and also for table bird production.

Chinese Painted eggs

The eggs are considerably smaller than those of the Coturnix quail. They are a dull bluish-grey in colour. In the wild, about a dozen eggs are produced in a season. In aviary bred and managed birds, this number will be increased to around 50, and the provision of artificial light will further increase the total. However, it is not usual to give Chinese Painted quail artificial light, as is the case with the Coturnix breeds, unless it is to produce early eggs for incubation.

The question is often asked: Can one eat the eggs? There is no reason why they should not be eaten, but they are much smaller than Coturnix eggs, and it seems hardly worth it. There is also the aspect that there is a ready market for Chinese Painted quail within the pet and aviary market, so it is much more profitable to incubate the eggs and sell the young through local pet shops.

Eggs for sale

If quails' eggs are to be produced for sale, then the best choice of breed is a commercial laying strain of Coturnix. If the enterprise is to be a reasonably large one, sufficient to provide an adequate income, then it is difficult to see how anything

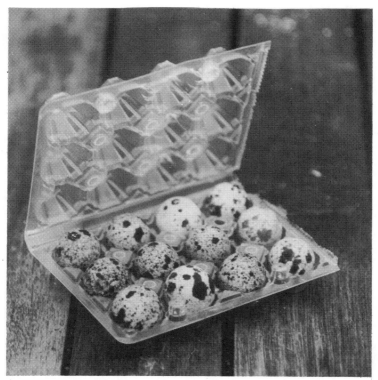

Purpose-made cartons are available for quails' eggs

other than a cage system or confined floor system, could be viable. The former is the most efficient in terms of management, as the eggs are easily collected. With a floor system, egg collection is more time-consuming and hazardous. Eggs tend to be laid anywhere and quails do not have a well-developed nest-laying instinct as do chickens. I have frequently stepped on eggs laid on the floor. They are small and the speckled nature of the shell has a camouflaging effect against the floor litter. In Britain, most quails' eggs are produced in cage systems while table birds are produced in floor systems similar to that used for broiler chickens.

Eggs should be collected at regular intervals on a daily basis and stored in a cool room at around 15⁰C. If any are to be incubated, it is best to select medium sized ones for this purpose, leaving the larger and smaller ones for sale. At present, there is no system of grading the eggs, as is the case with chickens' eggs offered for sale.

With a cage system, it is highly unlikely that there will be any problem of soiling of eggs. If there are any lightly soiled eggs it is best to brush them with a clean, dry nailbrush. Heavily soiled ones can be washed in warm water with a purpose-made egg sanitising solution, but it is best to avoid selling soiled eggs. If they are cleaned with a sanitising solution, they are suitable for incubation purposes. In fact, many commercial breeders fumigate or otherwise clean and disinfect hatching eggs as a matter of course, in order to avoid egg infection.

Packing and selling eggs

Eggs are sold in several ways. The fresh eggs frequently go to hotels, quality restaurants, delicatessens, farm-gate shops or other retail outlets.

Packaging is an important aspect of marketing and plastic egg cartons specifically for quail eggs are available from specialist suppliers.

If the quantity of cartons purchased is large enough, it is usually possible to have descriptive labels with details of your own farm incorporated. Alternatively, it is possible to order labels that you can stick on yourself. A company such as *Danro* can provide for all the labelling requirements.

Preserved eggs

A common form of egg marketing is to hard boil the eggs and put them in brine in a glass iar. The example shown in the photograph on page has six eggs in a jar with a metal crimped-on lid. This particular example is a product imported into the UK from France.

Pickled eggs are fairly common, as well as the use of them to produce a prepared product such as miniature Scotch eggs. Recipes are given later in the book.

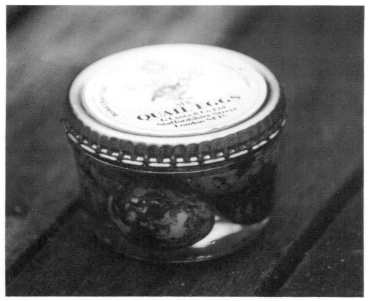
Quails' eggs boiled and preserved in brine, sold as a quality delicatessen product.

Winter eggs

The provision of artificial light in winter is essential if egg production is to continue without disruption.

In a small house, a 25 watt bulb is adequate for about 3 dozen birds and 40 watt for around 50. A 150 watt bulb with a reflector will be suffcient for a 20' x 10' building. Fluorescent tube lighting is also satisfactory. It is essential to incorporate a time-switch in the circuit so that the light is switched on and off automatically.

A total of 16 hours of light a day will keep egg production at satisfactory levels. Start giving extra light before dusk, gradually increasing the duration to compensate for the shortening days. Similarly, as the days lengthen, gradually decrease the amount of artificial light.

It is important to be consistent in turning on and switching off the light, and it is here that a pre-programmed time-switch is so valuable. In winter, the drop in temperature imposes more demands on the metabolism so that a certain proportion of energy is needed to keep warm. Bear this in mind and if necessary, increase the rations accordingly.

Quails for the table

In Britain, the same strains of Coturnix quail are used for egg production as well as for the table. In the USA, the Bobwhite is also raised for meat. Commercial battery systems and floor systems are used for rearing table birds, but the floor system is that most commonly used.

A house with a concrete floor is the most appropriate because of the dangers associated with rats which can kill adult quails with ease. Ridge ventilation in association with side windows is ideal, so that ventilation can be controlled. A very large house will probably rely on fan ventilation, but this should not be necessary if the tendency to overstock is resisted.

Many producers find that dividing a house into separate pens is better than having one large house. Quails are nervous birds and the tendency to panic and flap in one direction can lead to problems of management in this respect. An easy and relatively cheap way of subdividing the floor space is to use game netting, or some other form of lightweight panelling. Most game equipment suppliers sell such products.

Each pen or floor space needs wood shavings litter, a suspended or gravity-fed feeder, or one which the birds cannot scratch food out of, and ideally, an automatic watering system.

Young quail will have artificial heat as described in the breeding section, and as illustrated in the photograph on page 32. A certain proportion, or indeed all the females, may be separated for future egg production, leaving the males behind for table production.

The aim will be to produce quail with a liveweight of 6-7 oz at the age of 6 weeks, with a conversion ratio of around 3:1. In other words, for every three ounces of food consumed, around one ounce of weight is produced.

It is not feasible to weigh all the birds, of course, but it is a good idea to take a few sample weighings, using say half a dozen birds. This will give a general indication of the average weight of the batch.

The easiest way to weigh a quail is to use a small bag with a draw string at the top. The bird is popped into the bag, the draw strings tightened and then the whole thing is suspended

WEIGHINGS

Take sample weighings of about six birds per batch in order to have an average weight every week until it is time to slaughter them.

KEEPING RECORDS

Everyone has their own system of keeping records. The form of it is not important. What is necessary is to ensure that all the details in relation to weight gain and feed consumed are recorded.

DATE HATCHED:			NUMBER:_____
	AVERAGE LIVEWEIGHT	FEED CONSUMED	COMMENTS
WEEK 1			
WEEK 2			
WEEK 3			
WEEK 4			
WEEK 5			
WEEK 6			
WEEK 7			
WEEK 8:			
TOTAL			LOSSES:

on a spring balance. Those made by *Salter* are ideal. It takes only a moment or two, there is no distress caused to the bird, and it is released immediately after weighing. Those who prefer to use normal scales can utilize a polythene ice-cream carton - of the deep kind, or a cardboard shoe box. Pop in the quail and replace the lid, then place on the scales, remembering to subtract the known weight of the box from the total. Ready-made weighing cones and scales are also available from specialist suppliers.

Light restriction

Table quail grow more quickly and sexual development is slowed down if the amount of light to them is restricted. This does not mean that they have to be kept in a twilight zone, as is the case with so many poultry broilers, but no artificial light should be made available to them, as for egg producers. Some producers, I am afraid, go to absurd lengths in blocking out the light reaching the cages. I am against this on humanitarian grounds. Every creature has a right to natural light.

The aim is to cut down bright light, while allowing a certain amount of natural light to come in. This suppresses the urge to mate and to lay eggs so that growth continues uninterruptedly. In this way, much heavier weights are gained. Marsh Farms in the USA claimed that delaying the onset of lay until 12 weeks of age produced a doubling of normal bodyweight.

Killing, plucking and dressing

The usual method of killing is to sever the head in one quick movement. For this, a sharp butcher's knife or cleaver used in conjunction with a wooden block is suitable, although some producers find that sharp pruning shears are effective. Alternatively, poultry equipment suppliers sell a purpose-made poultry killer which operates on a guillotine principle.

Allow the bird to bleed, but it is not necessary to hang quail as it is with other game birds. Plucking should take place as quickly as possible, and here there are several alternatives.

Dry plucking

This is quite simply the removal of the feathers without using water or any other medium to assist the process. Plucking by hand can be a rapid process for those experienced in the field, but mechanical dry plucking machines are available where large quantities are involved.

Many people use these for the rough plucking, finishing off the pin feathers by hand, scraping or using a wax finish.

Plucked, gutted and dressed quails packaged ready for sale as fresh or frozen. Photograph by courtesy of Poultry World.

Wet plucking

Here, the bled birds are immersed in scalding water for a moment then removed and plucked as soon as possible. When plucking is complete, they are immersed in chilled water to cool.

Waxing

The principle of waxing is that the birds are dipped in molten wax and as this cools and hardens, the feathers come off with the wax crust. As referred to earlier, some producers use this method as a 'finishing' technique after initial rough plucking.

Once plucked, the birds are drawn. Traditionally, the innards were not removed and Mrs. Beeton would have frowned on such a practice. Modern susceptibilities however, demand that gutting is as complete as possible and commercial table quail will certainly need to be processed in this way, unless they are being sold to a butcher for processing.

Gutting is not as easy as it is with poultry, bearing in mind the relative smallness of the birds. I have found that utilising a spoon inserted in the neck end and rotating it inside the body cavity is as effective as anything. Cutting around the vent and enlarging the opening there then allows the innards to be drawn out. Some producers find this process too fiddly and time-consuming, and slit the birds down the back in order to gut them. Some complete the process by boning the birds at the same time, selling the finished product as 'boned quail'. On a large scale, vacuum drawing of the innards is carried out.

Once gutted, with the neck cut off close to the body and the legs cut off at the first joint up from the foot, the birds should be chilled again while awaiting packaging.

Packaging table quail

The usual way of packing quail is on polystyrene tray containers and covered with cling film sealed into position. A common procedure is to package four birds to each tray, arranged neatly, breast-side upwards. The photograph on the previous page shows ten birds packaged in this way, with a label showing the producer's name and the description that they are 'English bred quail'.

Oven-ready birds, as described above, can be sold fresh or frozen, depending on the particular market requirements. One great advantage of quail over game birds is that they are available right through the year, rather than on a seasonal basis. This is an important marketing point, in making 'game' dishes available to connoisseurs all through the year.

Smoked quail

A popular delicatessen commodity, smoked quail, is definitely for the top end of the market. If an enterprise is to be expanded in this direction, the best way is to arrange a contract with a local smoking company so that they do it in batches as necessary. Smoking of food is a skilled task and as there are EC directives with regard to safety, it is better to let a specialist company do it.

The recipes at the end give details of cooking quail to good effect. When selling direct to customers, as for example in a farm shop, being able to give them advice on how to cook them is important if they have not tried quail before.

Quail meat regulations

To sell quails for meat it is necessary to be familiar with the relevant hygiene regulations. These vary according to the scale of operations. From 1994 the regulations governing quails are likely to shadow fairly closely those for poultry, as changes in procedures and the bodies responsible are developed.

The starting point for information is to contact the *Meat Hygiene Advisor* at the local office of the Ministry of Agriculture, Fisheries and Food, who will explain what regulations are applicable in your particular case.

The regulations cover the slaughter and sale of fresh or frozen quail meat. Small scale operations, slaughtering less than 10,000 birds a year, will be exempt from *Directive 92/116*, but will be restricted to selling in their own localities and traditional markets. If you plan a larger operation, producing more than 10,000 but less than 150,000 birds, you qualify as a 'low throughput plant'. The more stringent regulations covering this, and larger scale operations, are available from the *Meat Hygiene Advisor*.

There are 'derogations', or temporary suspensions available, as well as different ways of conforming to the requirements, but as these are in a state of flux at the time of writing (December 1993), it is not possible to detail them here.

Finally, if you plan to export quails or quail meat, there are different regulations contained in the *Animal Health Circular 92/137* and *European Directive on Farmed Game 91/495*. Again, the local *Meat Hygiene Advisor* is there to help.

Marketing

Marketing is always the difficult aspect of any enterprise, particularly where the production side may take up most of one's time.

The main demand is for quails' eggs and table quail for the quality delicatessen market, although the potential sales of breeding stock should not be overlooked. The sales of ornamental breeds of quail can also provide a valuable side-line.

Local delicatessens, butchers, game dealers and hotels are obvious places to start. In fact starting on a small scale has much to recommend it. A farm shop on site is worth considering, as long as the site is in reasonable proximity to an urban or suburban area. *The Farm Shop and Pick Your Own Association* is worth contacting in this respect. Small local sales are also possible through local markets and the *Womens' Institute* markets.

If distribution further afield becomes a possibility - and here, production must be regular and consistent - it is important to contact specialist organisations such as *Food from Britain, The Delicatessen and Fine Foods Association* and the *Institute of Grocery Distribution.*

Specializing and turning the product into a 'value-added' one will give it even more distinctive value. Reference has already been made to the production of luxury items such as pickled eggs.

An aspect which is not often considered is to open part of the enterprise to the public, particularly if it is near an urban conurbation. A small area where different types of quail can be seen in aviary conditions, provides a source of interest. In conjunction with guided tours of the commercial production side, it can also provide a useful and educational experience for school parties.

On the question of diversification, the *Ministry of Agriculture's ADAS (Agricultural Development Advisory Service)* can provide help, advice and information, although consultancy services will be charged. The address of your nearest *ADAS* office will be in the local telephone directory or *Yellow Pages.*

Finance

For those intending to keep quail as a small business venture selling eggs, meat or breeding stock, there is the question of finance. Fortunately, setting up a quail unit is not very expensive, and it can be done on a step-by-step basis, expanding to meet demand. There are only a few big full-time quail enterprises in Britain. The others are on a smaller scale and are run on a part-time basis. There is nothing wrong with this. In fact, making use of empty farm buildings and sheds for a part-time enterprise such as this makes good economic sense. It is often a number of smaller enterprises which contribute to the success of an overall lifestyle.

As the aim is to make a profit, you need to have a detailed knowledge of all your costs. This will enable you to assess how to price your end products.

If the borrowing of money for expansion is required, the best place to begin is the bank. The manager will want to see your ideas in figures showing projected costs and sales. The very act of preparing such a plan will be useful and the bank manager's advice and experience should be helpful.

Do not neglect proper insurance covering your livestock, buildings, equipment, transport, etc. There are any number of companies who will provide appropriate cover and a good insurance broker should be able to help you.

There are also innumerable and useful guides to starting a business in good book shops.

Costs consist of *fixed costs* and *variable costs*. Fixed costs are large purchases like buildings, cages, feeders, drinkers and other things that last over a period of time. Fixed costs can spread over a period at so much per month, according to your estimate of their life and depreciation. Variable costs or running costs include everything else such as feed, transport, stock, heating etc. - in fact everything which can be regarded as a cost. Don't forget that everything that you use, particularly your car, can be assessed as a cost.

Keep careful note of all your costs in writing, including copies of all invoices that you pay. You should keep a ledger showing your sales and costs and keep it on a regular basis. You can obtain advice from your bank manager or accountant on this. You may find it easier to employ a part-time book-keeper who will keep everything in good order for a few hours work each month.

Finally, it should be remembered that a good accountant can be worth his or her weight in gold when it comes to advice. It would be a foolhardy person who started a business without one.

Health

Quails, like all living things, require good food, clean water, warm, dry and draught-free housing and regular attention. The main priority is always to prevent trouble and ill health, and to develop a ready eye for problems at an early stage. As soon as anything suspicious is noticed, such as listlessness, poor appetite, discharge from the beak or unusually coloured droppings, it is a good idea to isolate the bird immediately. This does two things; it stops the spread of possible infection to the others, and it allows the invalid a better chance of recovery. Listless birds often invite aggression and may be severely pecked by the others.

A hospital cage

A hospital cage is a useful thing to have. This could be a wooden bird breeding cage with a wire front, or even a large cardboard box. Specialist suppliers also sell purpose-made ones. Place some woodshavings in the bottom and clip on a feeder and drinker. The chances are that a sick bird will not be interested in the food, but it will certainly require water.

The cage should be in a warm, sheltered area, but if it is particularly cold, it may be a good idea to have a dull emitter bulb fixed up to provide a source of warmth. This can be placed outside the cage so that it is shining in sideways, through the cage front. Depending on the facilities available, it could be suspended from above. It is surprising how the provision of warmth and cosseting in this way, can sometimes make the difference between survival and loss, when all else possible has been done.

It is obviously not economic to call in the vet to see a single bird, although there is nothing to prevent you taking the cage with bird along to the vet. Where the condition is a minor one, such as a cold or simple digestive upset, it will clear up of its own accord, and the protected conditions help to make this sooner rather than later. If it is a more serious condition, there is not a lot to be done, and at least the bird will have met its end in relatively quiet comfort. If the bird is the first casualty in a more general outbreak, it enables action to be taken in time to protect the others.

Srong cardboard box fitted with a red or other dull emitter bulb

Ventilation holes

A temporary hospital cage. A more permanent one could be made in wood, with a front-opening glass or mesh door.

A hospital cage is a good idea. A bird which is off colour has a chance to recover in isolation from the others

Bacterial respiratory infections

Illnesses caused by bacteria can be treated with antibiotics, where viral ones can not. Some of the more common bacterial infections which affect the respiratory tract are bronchitis, pneumonia, infectious sinusitis and chronic respiratory disease. They all have similar symptoms of wheezing, laboured breathing, nasal discharge and loss of appetite.

An antibiotic such as *Neomycin* administered via the drinking water can be obtained from the vet. Again, it will be seen why a hospital cage is a good idea; the dosing of the water supply is made simpler.

Bacterial digestive infections

There are several of these conditions that can be detected by the listlessness of the bird, lack of appetite and nature of the droppings. Enteritis results in greenish droppings. Coccidiosis also produces greenish droppings but of a more slimy nature.

Again, antibiotic treatment is required and the vet will prescribe an appropriate one such as *Terramycin*, for dosing the drinking water.

Salmonella is always a danger, and every effort should be made to avoid it. Make sure that all feeders and drinkers are cleaned regularly and thoroughly, and that feedstuffs are fresh and clean.

Worms

Internal worms may be a problem with quail which are aviary housed, or which have access to the soil via pens. The importance of moving pens to fresh, clean ground on a regular basis is obvious, as well as the practice of liming aviary soil each autumn while the birds are in their winter quarters.

Caged quails are unlikely to have worm problems because they are not in a position to ingest the cysts which produce them.

Internal worms cause emaciation and loss of feather condition, and any permanent quail breeding stock which has access to the ground, should be wormed as a matter of course before being brought in for the winter. Again, it is a matter of dosing the drinking water with a vermifuge such as *Thiabenzole,* which is available from the vet.

Scaly leg

This is a condition of the legs, where burrowing mites push up the scales of the legs and produce white encrustations. It is highly infectious and will spread rapidly to all the birds if not treated quickly.

Using an old toothbrush and warm soapy water, brush off the encrustations, then dry the legs before applying *Benzyl benzoate* which is available from the vet. This is most effective and far better than the traditional paraffin treatment. Do not try and pull the dry encrustations away otherwise the skin itself is pulled away.

Bumblefoot

A hard lump can sometimes form underneath the foot, where a small wound may have healed over leaving some infection behind. It is first detected when a bird is seen to be limping. If the infection is still active, the foot will feel hot and swollen and antibiotic treatment is needed.

If the lump is near the surface, it can be lanced to remove the pus, then treated with any disinfectant cream.

Wounds

Any wounds such as those acquired by head banging or fighting should be cleaned and treated with antiseptic cream or disinfectant. Keep the bird in isolation until the wound has healed, in case it is pecked by the others.

Mites

Quail can be affected by mites in the same way that poultry can become infested. Red mite is a particular problem.

Proprietary insecticide powder is the answer, dusted under the wings and around the neck and rump feathers. It is available from most poultry and pet suppliers. Don't forget to dust the housing and dustbath areas as well!

Breeding problems

Reference has already been made to the necessity of housing good breeding stock and not to interbreed closely related strains, unless you know that they are free of defects. If the introduction of females to males is carried out carefully, there is usually no problem, although it does occasionally happen that a male will refuse to accept a female.

I once had a Coturnix layer who was constantly driven away by the male (she was part of a trio), and he devoted all his attentions to the other one. He would not mate with her but pecked her unmercifully. I eventually had to take her away and put her in solitary confinement. Her wounds healed and she seemed fit and healthy, with a good appetite, when without warning she died. I have often wondered whether the male knew more than I did, and whether there is some instinctive survival mechanism which operates with discrimination in these cases.

An aspect which is frequently forgotten is that breeding birds do need an excellent and well-balanced diet, otherwise a nutritional deficiency may manifest in weakly chicks. Clubbed feathers and leg problems in the chicks are frequently associated with an inadequate level of minerals and vitamins in the parent stock.

The only other problem which is likely to occur is that of egg binding, where a female occasionally is seen to sit for long periods of time without laying an egg. The best solution, as with other poultry, is to hold her over steam (a bowl of hot water - but take care not to drop her), and gently massage the vent with vaseline. This is really all that is possible for if the egg breaks inside her, it invariably leads to death. Although infection is usually given as the reason why death occurs, it seems to me that shock plays a major part, for a bird can die before infection has had a chance to develop.

I have already referred to possible problems with young quail. If a good level of hygiene and incubation practice is maintained, problems will be minimised. The incubator and brooder area needs complete cleaning and disinfecting after use and before a new batch of eggs and young are introduced. Most problems with poor hatches are usually connected with one of the following reasons: poor breeding stock, low fertility of parents, poor standard of nutrition in parents, infection in eggs caused by poor standards of hygiene, temperature fluctuations, humidity fluctuations or inadequate turning of the eggs.

Feather pecking

This is an old problem in the poultry world and everyone seems to have their favourite remedies, from sprinkling pepper to beak trimming. I am certainly against the latter practice on humanitarian grounds.

Check that there is no mite problem, and that feeding and watering levels are adequate. Over-crowding and lack of interest in the environment are often contributory agents.

A bird which is being pecked regularly, or one that is a persistent attacker, should be separated for a time so that the habit can be broken.

Notifiable diseases

Finally, quail can be affected by Newcastle disease or Fowl pest, although it is primarily found in chickens. Symptoms are paralysis of the legs and throwing the head backwards. It is a notifiable disease in Britain so the vet or local office of the Ministry of Agriculture should be notified.

Recipes

It is not necessary to hang quail as it is with other game birds, merely to allow it to bleed after the head has been removed. Traditionally, the innards were not removed and Mrs. Beeton would have frowned on such a practice. Modern susceptibilities, however, demand that gutting is as complete as possible, and I have already referred to the fact that it is common commercially, for the birds to be split down the back, or for a vacuum procedure to be used.

Mrs Beeton's recipe

Ingredients: Quails, butter, toast.
Method: These birds keep good for several days and should be roasted without drawing (but not if you have modern susceptibilities - see above). Truss them with the legs close to the body, and the feet pressing upon the thighs. Place some slices of toast in the dripping pan, allowing a piece of toast for each bird. Roast for 15-20 minutes; keep them well basted and serve on the toast.

Quick roast quail

This is my favourite way of cooking them and the bacon adds to the flavour, as well as preventing too much drying.
Ingredients: Quail, 2 slices of bacon per bird.
Method: Wrap up each bird in the bacon and use wooden sausage sticks to keep them in place. Roast in a medium oven for about 20 minutes and serve with any of the sauces or garnishes normally used with chicken or game.

Grilled quail

Ingredients: Quail, butter, lemon juice, bacon slices, salt and black pepper, breadcrumbs.
Method: Slit each quail down the backbone. (A strong pair of scissors is adequate for this.) Flatten each side and sprinkle with lemon juice, salt and pepper. Dip in melted butter and

roll in breadcrumbs. Grill for about 5-6 minutes on each side. Meanwhile, roll up the bacon slices and grill them for the last few minutes with the quail. Serve quails with bacon rolls and garnish with mushrooms.

French roast quail

Ingredients: Quail, butter, vine leaves, toast, salt, black pepper, milk.

Method: Wipe quail inside and out. Place in a saucepan with just enough milk to cover them. Simmer gently for 6-7 minutes. Remove and put the saucepan and its contents to one side for the moment.

Smear the quail with butter and wrap them in vine leaves. Sprinkle with salt and pepper and place in a buttered ovenproof dish. Roast for 10 minutes in a medium oven, then take the dish out of the oven. Strain the contents of the saucepan and pour over the quail. Replace the dish in the oven and cook for another 10 minutes. Serve each quail on a slice of toast and garnish with wedges of lemon and sprigs of parsley.

Miniature Scotch eggs

An enterprising British quail egg producer has evolved a novel way of giving his eggs value-added appeal. He hardboils them, removes the shells, coats them in flour and sausagemeat, with a final coating of breadcrumbs. Once deep-fried for a few moments, they provide miniature Scotch eggs, a delicacy which has obvious appeal for the delicatessen market.

Pickled eggs

Quails' eggs are so attractive that many people hard boil and serve them in their shells. An alternative is to preserve or pickle them in one of the folowing ways:

Whole eggs in brine This is a compromise where the eggs are first hard boiled and then placed in a brine solution without removing the shells.

A normal brine solution of 50g salt per 600ml of water (2oz per pint) is suitable. Hard boil the eggs, drain and place them in sterilised jars and top up with the brine solution, making sure that they are completely covered. (Jars can be sterilised by washing in hot water, then placing upside down on a rack in a warm oven, leaving the door open).

Home Farm pickled eggs   This is the recipe that I used for my quails' eggs. Hard boil the eggs, then plunge into cold water to cool and make them easier to peel. (Note that fresh eggs are more difficult to peel than older ones, so don't use fresh eggs for pickling).

Peel the eggs then place them into sterilised glass jars and top up with a pickling solution made as follows: Place 2 pints of white vinegar and a pint of water in a stainless steel saucepan. (You can leave out or reduce the water if you like a 'tangy' egg, but it does mean that the more delicate egg flavour is dominated by the vinegar). If you have just a few eggs, reduce the ingredient amounts accordingly.

Add 2 level tablespoons of salt, a medium sized chopped onion and 1 oz of pickling spice (2oz if you like them particularly spicy), and bring to the boil. Simmer for a few minutes, then leave to cool and strain. Pour over the eggs, then pop in a few of the boiled peppercorns just to make the jar look a bit more interesting.

Oak Ridge pickled eggs   This is a recipe from Max and Mary Crawley of Arkansas, USA, and I am grateful to Edmund Hoffman for the information.

Boil the eggs for five minutes in water to which the following have been added: ½ cup of salt and 1 fluid oz of vinegar per gallon of water. Cool in cold water and peel the eggs, then place them in sterilised jars.

Prepare the pickling solution as follows: add 1 cup of salt and 1 large chopped onion (with other spices if liked) to two pints of white vinegar and two pints of water. Bring to the boil, drain and pour over the eggs.

Large scale pickled eggs   This recipe is more appropriate to large producers. Hardboil the eggs and then place them (covered) in commercial grade, distilled white vinegar for 12 hours. This dissolves the shells, but leaves the membranes intact. Wash the eggs and refrigerate until quite cold then immerse in clean water while the membranes are removed by hand. They are now ready for immersing in the pickling solution of your choice.

Quails' eggs in aspic

Quails' eggs in aspic is, of course, a well-known delicacy and another way of achieving the maximum return on the eggs if they are to be sold.

The eggs are hard boiled, then shelled. They can be cracked, placed in cold water and have the shells and membranes removed simultaneously.

If cut in half and placed in a small glass or plastic container with the yolk facing upwards, the aspic mixture can then be poured on. Once set and cooled, clear snap-on lids can be placed on the container, enabling the product to be seen. If the container is small containing, for example, four halves, it is a perfect individual hors d'oeuvres, and can be marketed as such.

Coturnix laying quail in 'natural' surroundings.

References

Bibliography

QUAIL:THEIR BREEDING AND MANAGEMENT. G.E.S.Robbins.World Pheasant Association 1984 (UK).

DOMESTIC QUAIL FOR HOBBY AND PROFIT. G.E.S. Robbins. A.B. Incubators. 1989 (UK)

QUAIL MANUAL. Albert F. Marsh. Marsh Farm Publications. 1976 (USA)

RAISING BOBWHITE QUAIL FOR COMMERCIAL USE. Circular 514. Clemson University & U.S. Department of Agriculture. 1964 (USA).

THAT QUAIL, ROBERT. Margaret Stranger. J.B. Lippincott Co. 1966 (USA) Hodder & Stoughton. 1967 (UK).

ORNAMENTAL BIRDS. Stanislav Chvapil. Hamlyn. 1983. (UK).

THE ATLAS OF QUAILS. David Alderton T.F.H. Publications 1992 (USA)

COTURNIX QUAIL. Edmund Hoffmann. Self-published. 1988 (Canada)

INCUBATION. A GUIDE TO HATCHING AND REARING. Katie Thear. Broad Leys Publishing. 1987 (UK)

THE COMPLETE BOOK OF RAISING LIVESTOCK AND POULTRY. Katie Thear. Pan Books 1988 (UK)

HOME FARM, Broad Leys Publishing Co., Buriton House, Station Road, Newport, Saffron Walden, Essex CB11 3PL Tel: 0799 540 922 Fax: 0799 541 367 - Britain's small farming journal, with articles on quail and poultry.

POULTRY WORLD, Carew House, Wallington. Surrey SM6 ODX - Magazine for the poultry industry.

CAGE AND AVIARY BIRDS, IPC Magazines, Kings Reach Tower, Stamford Street, London SE99 0BB - Newspaper for cage and aviary bird enthusiasts.

Suppliers of quail breeds

CLARENCE COURT LTD., PO Box 2, Winchcombe, Glos GL54 5YA. Tel: 0242 621 228 or 0831 849 036. - Breeding stock and point of lay Japanese quail.

CURFEW COTURNIX QUAIL, Buttons Hill, Southminster Road, Althorne, Essex CM3 6EN. Tel: 0621 741 923 - 'Crusader' strain of commercial Coturnix quail.

FAYRE GAME, Lodge Lane Nurseries, Lodge Lane, Lytham, Lancashire FY8 5RP. Tel: 0253 738 640 - Japanese, English White, American Range, Tuxedo, Fawn Coturnix quail.

GRANGE AVIARIES & PET CENTRE, Hillier Garden Centre, Woodhouse Lane, Botley, Southampton SO3 2EZ. Tel: 0489 781 260 - Chinese Painted, Californian, Bobwhite and Coturnix quail.

NEWMARKET AVIARIES, Newmarket Lane, Clay Lane, Clay Cross, Chesterfield, Derbyshire. Tel: (0246) 863 506 - Bobwhite, Mountain, Mexican Speckled, Mexican Blue Scaled, Gambel, Californian and the new mutations of the Chinese Painted quail, including Pure White, Gold, Silver, Normal Pearled, and Pied.

QUAIL WORLD, Glenydd, Penrhiwllan, Llandysul, Dyfed SA44 5NR. Tel: (0559) 370 105 - Japanese, Gold, Tuxedo, White, Chinese Painted, Gambel, Californian quail.

SHROPSHIRE BIRD AND AQUATIC CENTRE, Broughall, Whitchurch, Shropshire SY13 4AB. Tel: (0948) 662 651 - Chinese Painted, Japanese, Bobwhite, Californian quail.

Equipment and supplies

ASD COURT STEEL, Thames Wharf Dock Road, London E16 1AF. Tel: 071 476 0444 Fax: 071 476 0239 - Aviary meshes.

ASH AND LACY MONCASTERS, Belvoir Way, Fairfield Industrial Estate, Louth, Lincs LN1 0JG. Tel: 0507 600 666 - Aviary meshes.

BHT POULTRY HOUSING, 'Welwin', Rawcliffe Road, Goole, North Humberside DN14 8JN. Tel: 0405 764 715 - Haybox brooder house.

BRINSEA INCUBATORS, Station Road, Sandford, Avon BS19 5RA. Tel: 0934 823 039 - Incubators and brooders.

CLARENCE COURT LTD, PO Box 2, Winchcombe, Glos GL54 5YA. Tel: 0242 621 228 or (0831) 849 036 - Quail egg boxes.

CURFEW INCUBATORS, Buttons Hill, Southminster Road, Althorne, Essex CM3 6EN. Tel: 0621 741 923 - Incubators, quail cages, brooders, header tanks, drinking systems, feeders.

DANRO LTD., Unit 68, Jaydon Industrial Estate, Station Road, Earl Shilton, Leicester LE9 7GA. Tel: 0455 847 061/2. Fax: 0455 841 272 - Labels for egg boxes and produce, hand-held labellers, sealing tape and cartons.

ECOSTAT ELECTRONIC CONTROLS & THERMOSTAT COMPANY, Bosleake Industrial Estate, Carn Brea, Redruth, Cornwall TR15 3YG. Tel: 0209 612 033. Fax: 0209 612 264 - Incubators, DIY incubator kits, digital thermometers, incubator spares and conversion kits.

GAMEKEEPA FEEDS LTD, Southerly Park, Binton, Stratford-upon-Avon, Warks CV37 9TU. Tel: 0789 772 429. Fax: 0789 490 536. - Quail feeds, incubators and equipment.

GRANGE AVIARIES & PET CENTRE, Hillier Garden Centre, Woodhouse Lane, Botley, Southampton S03 2EZ. Tel: 0489 781 260. - Aviaries, aviary panels, mesh and cages.

MANOR FARM GRANARIES, Brington, Huntingdon, Cambs PE18 0PY. Tel: 08014 235/639. Fax: 08014 326 - 'Quail Mix' feed, incubators, cages and equipment.

QUAIL WORLD, Glenydd, Penrhiwllan, Llandysul, Dyfed SA44 5NR. Tel: 0559 370 105 - Incubators, pens, drinkers and feeders.

SHROPSHIRE BIRD AND AQUATIC CENTRE, Broughall, Whitchurch, Shropshire SY13 4AB. Tel: 0948 662 651 - Aviaries, breeding cages, equipment.

SOUTHERN AVIARIES, Tinkers Lane, Hadlow Down, Uckfield, East Sussex TN22 4EU. Tel: 0825 830 283 Fax: 0825 830 241 - Aviaries, meshes, cages, incubators and equipment.

TORNE VALLEY LTD, Bawtry Road, Tickhill, Doncaster DN11 9EX. Tel: 0302 751 500 - Incubators, brooders and equipment.

Index

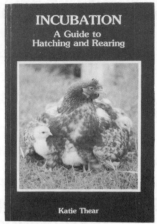